HOUGHTON

Reading

A Legacy of Literacy

Talent
Show

HOUGHTON MIFFLIN   BOSTON • MORRIS PLAINS, NJ

California • Colorado • Georgia • Illinois • New Jersey • Texas

Printed in the U.S.A.

ISBN 0-618-16212-7

56789-BS-07 06 05 04 03

Design, Art Management, and Page Production: Silver Editions.

Contents

Our Classroom Zoo Book

by Linda Dunlap
illustrated by Mick Reid

Miss Moon's class made a zoo book.
It took us hours in the art room.

1

Miss Moon has cool art tools! We
drew with pencils and markers. We
found paints in every color, or hue. We
shared the paints to be fair. We also
used glue and paper. We even made
our own paste!

I drew a moose with droopy eyes.
That moose looked sad! I just knew I
would paint him blue.

Lou made a cool trout. She drew that
trout with sparkling glue! Then she
painted it gold inside the glue lines. She
might paint a bunch of those trout!

Mansoor drew a very good goose. He saw a goose land on the ground. The goose stood very still. Mansoor looked at that goose while he drew. But then that goose flew away.

Sue drew zoo workers. One woman
was cleaning with a broom. Another
zoo helper was cooking food. It looked
like they were having a good time.

6

Miss Moon keeps our zoo book in our room. We add new art too. That zoo book makes us proud.

Jade's Drumming

by Melissa Blackwell Burke

illustrated by Ruth Flanigan

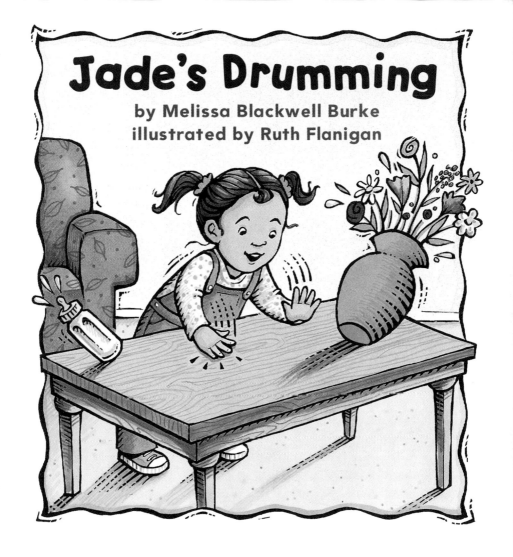

Tap! Tap! Tap! Tap! Tap! Tap!
When Jade was a baby, she began
drumming. She rapped and tapped
and patted on everything.

9

When Jade grew up some, she still
drummed. She drummed when she was
planning her day. She drummed when
she was shopping. She drummed when
she was sitting in the tub. Jade was
forever drumming.

"You're bugging me with so much drumming," her sister would say.

But Jade never stopped. She just kept right on drumming.

"I like the sound," Jade would say. "Don't you like it too?"

At times her mother would say, "Jade, the baby is napping. Would you please stop drumming?"

Jade would say, "Yes, Mom, I will stop." Then she would drum outside.

12

When Jade and her sister rode the
bus, Jade would do her drumming. It
didn't matter if Jade's sister grabbed her
drumsticks. Jade would just start patting
her lap or tapping on the window.

"You're bugging me with so much
drumming," her sister would say.

"I'm sorry," Jade would say. "I just
like the sound so much."

When Jade grew up, she did become
a very good drummer. She asked her
sister to go to a show. Her sister
nodded, and off they went.

At the show, Jade did her drumming.

Her sister did not say that Jade was
bugging her with so much drumming.
Instead, she clapped and bragged,
"That's my sister drumming!"

Jade waved to the crowd. The crowd stood up and clapped and clapped.

Jade's drumming made a lot of people very happy!

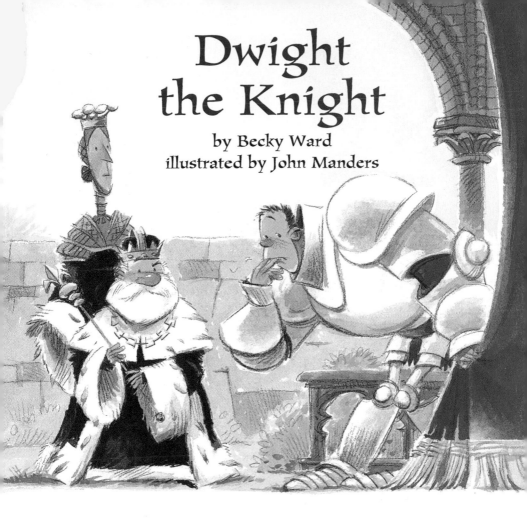

Dwight
the Knight

by Becky Ward
illustrated by John Manders

Sir Dwight had many talents. Queen Fair and King Mighty felt that Sir Dwight served them very well indeed. There was just one problem. Sir Dwight would not fight.

17

"My heart is not in it. This knight just can't fight," said Sir Dwight.

"But knights must fight," insisted King Mighty. "That is what knights do."

"Well, that is not what this knight does," said Sir Dwight. "Must I serve you in battle? I am able to serve you in so many other ways."

"I can fix you a feast and do it up
right. I'll stir up a fine beef stew and
then bake you my best lemon pie," said
Sir Dwight brightly.

"Sir Dwight, you are a fine cook," said
Queen Fair. "But knights must go out
and fight."

19

"I can tell you my best stories each night at bedtime. My mind is filled with wonderful tales. Some will delight you and others will fill you with fright," said Sir Dwight.

"Sir Dwight, we really like the way you tell tales," said King Mighty. "But knights must go out and fight."

"I can paint you pictures of beautiful sights," said Sir Dwight.

"And your paintings are delightful," said the queen. "But really, Sir Dwight, knights must go out and fight."

"I can say the alphabet while I dance a jig. I can run like lightning each time you call. I can stitch you silk sheets that make sweet dreams each night," said Sir Dwight.

The knight went down on his knees. "I will try to grow wings and then take flight. But please, please, PLEASE don't make me fight," cried Sir Dwight.

"Greetings, Holly," said Tom, the owner of Tom's Toys. He was placing three toy bears below a bench outside his shop.

"Good day," Holly replied, waving.

"Look out!" Tom shouted, but it was too late.

Crash! Holly wiped out just past Tom's store.

Then King Mighty spoke, "All right, Sir Dwight. It is not right to make you fight if you can't. Tell me, can you be a stay-at-home knight and serve us with your fine talents?"

Sir Dwight hugged King Mighty. "Yes, yes, yes! Yes I can!" he cried.

And that's what he did for the rest of his life!

Will Holly Sing?

by Anne Walker
illustrated by Anne Kennedy

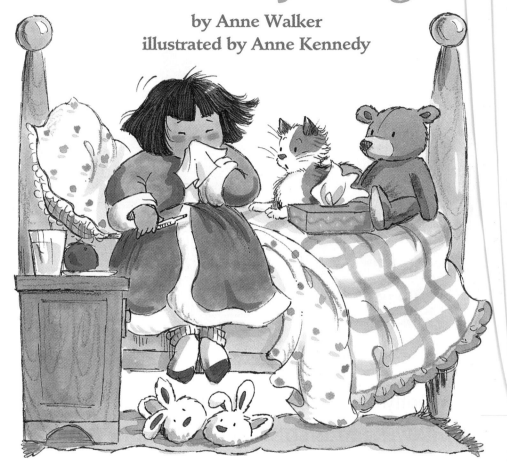

Holly sat up in bed.

"My cold is horrible," whined Holly.

Then she sneezed.

"I hope I can sing at the show."

So you see, it is true. It takes time
and talent to draw a cartoon. Can
you think up an idea for a funny
cartoon? Maybe you will invent a
new comic strip!

Last, the artist chooses colors for the
cartoon. He picks bright shades of blue,
green, red, and yellow. Then he sends
the comic strip to be printed.

After that, the artist traces his pencil
lines with ink. He uses fine pens,
brushes, and art tools for adding lines
and dots that look like shadows. An
artist can cut out and glue patterns on
the cartoon, too.

Then the artist draws in the
background. Some cartoon drawings
need lines to show the walls in a room.
Others need the moon or a few trees
and clouds.

Next the artist sketches the main
things that go in each box of the cartoon
strip. He uses pencil in case he goofs!
He draws balloons and writes words
in them, too.

Who Drew the Cartoon?

by Becky Ward
illustrated by Len Epstein

When you look at a cartoon strip, do you ever wonder who drew it? An artist with lots of talent spent a long time drawing that cartoon!

First, an artist has to think up a funny
story to tell. Then he plans what will go
in each drawing.

26

Tom raced to help Holly up.

She felt a little dazed. She stroked her scraped leg.

Then she shook her head.

"Are you all right?" Tom asked.

"I'm super!" Holly replied. "My head feels better."

"So falling down fixed things up!" joked Tom.

Tom helped her inside his shop. He gave her some freshly baked apple pie.

That night Holly sang in the show.

Smiling, she said, "My first number is for Tom and Luke."

Then she sang "Good Friends."

Fright Night

by Anne Walker
illustrated by Sarah Brittain

Miss Knight's class was getting set
for Fright Night. They hung a banner
outside the school.

"Fright Night will be the best night
this year," cried Betsy. "I can't wait."

Many people came to see the show
for Fright Night. Mothers and fathers
found seats. Bright lights shone on the
stage. Miss Knight said, "Steve Gilbert
will go first."

Steve sat in the spotlight on Miss Knight's stool. He wore a green tie. He told a tale. In this tale a creature named Mighty Max lived in the woods. A brave boy made friends with this creature, and found out he was as gentle as a lamb.

Next, it was Sally's turn. Sally told about the high flight of six bats. She showed pictures of real bats. Then she yelled "BOO!" and ran off the stage.

Kenny dressed up for his spider dance. He was quite a sight. He wore a black cape cut in strips. The strips hung like a spider's legs. Kenny finished his dance and bowed.

Sue and Shelly wore matching dresses
with bright red tights. They tossed three
glowing tubes back and forth like jugglers.
Then Sue sang a spooky tune while Shelly
played the sax.

46

The show ended with a tune sung by the whole class. The parents stood up and clapped. Everyone asked to have Fright Night again next year.

"We just might do that," sighed Miss Knight.

Word List

Theme 6

Our Classroom Zoo Book (p. 1) accompanies *The Art Lesson.*

DECODABLE WORDS

Target Skill

Vowel Pairs *ew, oo, ou, ue*

blue, book, broom, classroom, cooking, cool, drew, droopy, flew, food, found, glue, good, goose, ground, hue, knew, looked, Lou, Mansoor, Moon, Moon's, moose, new, proud, room, stood, Sue, too, took, tools, trout, zoo

Words Using Previously Taught Skills

add, and, away, art, at, be, bunch, but, class, cleaning, has, having, he, helper, him, in, inside, it, just, keeps, land, like, lines, made, makes, markers, might, Miss, on, or, paints, paint, painted, paste, pencils, sad, saw, shared, she, sparkling, still, that, then, those, time, us, used, very, we, while, with

HIGH-FREQUENCY WORDS

New

fair, gold, woman

Previously Taught

a, also, another, color, even, every, eyes, flour, hours, I, of, one, our, own, paper, school, the, they, to, was, were, workers, would

Jade's Drumming (p. 9) accompanies *The Art Lesson.*

Target Skill (Review)
Structural Analysis: Base Words and Endings -*ed, -ing*
bragged, bugging, clapped, drummed, drumming, grabbed, napping, nodded, patted, patting, planning, rapped, shopping, sitting, stopped, tapped, tapping

Words Using Previously Taught Skills
and, asked, at, bus, but, crowd, day, did, didn't, drum, drummer, drumsticks, forever, go, good, grew, happy, her, if, in, is, it, Jade, Jade's, just, kept, lap, like, lot, made, matter, me, mom, mother, much, my, never, not, on, or, outside, please, right, rode, say, she, show, sister, so, sorry, sound, start, still, stood, stop, tap, that, that's, then, times, too, tub, up, very, waved, went, when, will, with, window, yes, you

HIGH-FREQUENCY WORDS

Previously Taught
a, baby, become, began, do, don't, everything, I, I'm, instead, of, off, people, some, the, they, to, was, would, you're

Dwight the Knight (p. 17) accompanies *Moses Goes to a Concert.*

DECODABLE WORDS

Target Skill
Long *i (igh, ie)*
brightly, cried, delight, delightful, Dwight, fight, flight, fright, knight, knights, lightning, mighty, night, pie, right, sights

Words Using Previously Taught Skills
able, am, and, at, bake, battle, be, bedtime, beef, best, but, can, can't, cook, dance, did, don't, down, dreams, each, feast, felt, fill, filled, fine, fix, for, go, grow, had, he, his, home, hugged, if, in, indeed, insisted, is, it, jig, just, king, knees, lemon, life, like, make, me, must, my, not, on, out, paint, paintings, pictures, please, problem, queen, really, rest, run, say, serve, served, sheets, silk, sir, so, spoke, stay, stew, stir, stitch, sweet, take, talents, tales, tell, that, that's, them, then, this, time, try, up, us, very, way, ways, we, well, went, while, will, wings, with, wonderful, yes, you

HIGH-FREQUENCY WORDS

New
alphabet, heart, mind

Previously Taught
a, all, are, beautiful, call, do, does, fair, head, I, I'll, many, of, one, other, others, said, some, stories, the, there, to, was, what, would, your

Who Drew the Cartoon? (p. 25) accompanies *Moses Goes to a Concert.*

DECODABLE WORDS

Target Skill (Review)
Vowel Pairs *ew, oo, ou, ue*

balloons, blue, cartoon, chooses, drew, few, glue, goofs, moon, new, room, too, tools, true, you

Words Using Previously Taught Skills
adding, after, an, and, art, artist, at, background, be, box, bright, brushes, can, case, clouds, comic, cut, dots, draw, drawing, drawings, draws, each, ever, fine, first, for, funny, go, green, has, he, his, in, ink, invent, is, it, last, like, lines, look, lots, main, maybe, need, next, on, or, out, patterns, pencil, pens, picks, plans, printed, red, see, sends, shades, shadows, show, sketches, so, spent, strip, takes, talent, that, tell, them, then, things, think, time, traces, trees, up, uses, when, will, with, wonder, writes, yellow

HIGH-FREQUENCY WORDS

Previously Taught

a, colors, do, idea, long, of, others, some, story, the, to, walls, what, who, words

Will Holly Sing? (p. 33) accompanies *The School Mural.*

DECODABLE WORDS

Target Skill
Base Words and Endings -*ed*, -*ing*
baked, dazed, glided, joked, laced, placing, raced, scraped, skating, smiling, sneezed, stroked, waving, wheezed, whined, wiped

Words Using Previously Taught Skills
advice, and, apple, asked, at, band, bed, bench, better, but, can, crash, day, down, drug, Elmer's, explained, feels, felt, first, fixed, for, fresh, freshly, gave, good, greetings, hardware, he, help, helped, her, his, Holly, hope, horrible, how, in, inside, is, it, just, late, leg, little, look, Luke, mom, my, night, number, out, outside, owner, past, pie, replied, right, sang, sat, see, she, shook, shop, shopping, shouted, show, sing, skates, so, soon, soup, spend, still, stopped, store, super, that, then, things, three, Tom, Tom's, too, town, toy, toys, up, went, while, will, you

HIGH-FREQUENCY WORDS

New
below, neighbor, should

Previously Taught
a, air, all, are, bears, cold, falling, friends, head, hear, I, I'm, of, said, some, the, to, warm, was, your

Fright Night **(p. 41)** accompanies *The School Mural.*

Target Skill (Review)

Long *i* as *igh, ie*

bright, cried, flight, fright, high, Knight, Knight's, lights, might, mighty, night, sighed, sight, spotlight, tie, tights

Previously Taught

about, and, as, asked, back, banner, bats, be, best, Betsy, black, boo, bowed, boy, brave, by, came, can't, cape, clapped, class, creature, cut, dance, dressed, dresses, ended, fathers, finished, first, for, forth, found, gentle, getting, Gilbert, glowing, go, green, he, his, hung, in, it, jugglers, just, Kenny, lamb, legs, like, made, matching, Max, Miss, mothers, named, next, on, out, outside, parents, pictures, played, quite, ran, real, red, Sally, Sally's, sang, sat, sax, seats, see, set, she, Shelly, shone, show, showed, six, spider, spider's, spooky, stage, Steve, stood, stool, strips, Sue, sung, tale, that, then, this, three, tossed, tubes, tune, turn, up, wait, we, while, whole, will, with, woods, wore, yelled

HIGH-FREQUENCY WORDS

Previously Taught

a, again, do, everyone, friends, have, I, lived, many, of, off, people, said, school, the, they, to, told, was, year

HIGH-FREQUENCY WORDS TAUGHT TO DATE:

Grade 1							
a	carry	friend	long	pull	today	believe	move
able	caught	full	look	put	together	below	neighbor
about	children	funny	love	read	too	between	order
above	cling	garden	many	ready	try	board	pair
afraid	cold	girl	me	right	turn	bought	poor
after	color	give	minute	room	two	brother	quiet
again	come	go	more	said	under	brought	reason
against	could	goes	morning	saw	upon	busy	roll
all	cow	gone	most	school	very	care	should
already	dance	good	mother	second	walk	child	soldier
also	divide	green	my	see	wall	clothes	special
always	do	grow	near	seven	want	different	stand
and	does	happy	never	shall	warm	during	story
animal	done	hard	not	sharp	was	early	straight
any	door	have	now	she	wash	even	surprise
are	down	he	ocean	shoe(s)	watched	fair	told
arms	draw	head	of	shout	water	field	touch
around	eat	hear	off	show	we	floor	trouble
away	edge	her	old	sing	wear	front	uncle
baby	eight	here	on	small	were	gold	until
bear	else	hold	once	so	what	great	war
because	enough	horse	one	some	where	guess	weigh
been	evening	house	only	soon	who	hair	whole
before	ever	how	open	start	why	half	winter
began	every	hungry	or	sure	work	heard	woman
begin	fall	hurt	other	table	world	heart	word
bird	family	I	our	talk	would	heavy	year
blue	far	idea	out	tall	write	hour	young
body	father	in	over	teacher	you	important	
both	find	is	own	the	your	instead	
break	first	jump	paper	their		kitchen	
brown	five	kind	part	there	**Grade 2**	lady	
build	flower	know	people	these	across	later	
butter	fly	laugh	person	they	ago	letter	
buy	follow	learn	picture	thought	air	lion	
by	for	light	piece	three	alphabet	listen	
call	forest	like	play	through	aunt	middle	
car	found	little	present	tiny	beautiful	million	
	four	live	pretty	to	behind	mind	

Decoding Skills Taught to Date: Short Vowels *a, i;* Base Words and Endings *–s, -ed, -ing;* Short Vowels *o, u, e;* Structural Analysis: VCCV Pattern; Long Vowels *a, i* (CVC*e*); Long Vowels *o, u, e* (CVC*e*); Two Sounds for *g;* Consonant Clusters *r, l, s;* Two Sounds for *c;* Double Consonants; Structural Analysis: VCV Pattern; Consonant Digraphs *th, wh, sh, ch, (tch);* Base Words and Endings *–er, -est;* Vowel Pairs *ai, ay;* Compound Words; Vowel Pairs *ow, ou;* Suffixes *–ly, -ful;* Vowel Pairs *ee, ea;* Common Syllables *–tion, –ture;* r-Controlled Vowels *ar, or, ore;* Words with *nd, nt, mp, ng, nk;* Base Words and Endings *-s, -es, -ies;* Vowel Pairs *oa, ow;* The *–er* Ending in Two-Syllable Words; Contractions; The *–le* Ending in Two-Syllable Words; Sound of *y* at the End of Longer Words; Prefix *un–;* Base Words and Endings *–ed, –ing* (Double Final Consonant); Silent Consonants *gh, kn, b;* Vowel Pairs *oo, ew, ue, ou;* Long *i* as *igh, ie;* Base Words and Endings *–ed, –ing* (Drop Final *e*)